Series Editor **Ian Denley**

Scales and Arpeggios for Clarinet

Grades 1-8

It is often maintained, with some justification, that wind-players frequently show reluctance to learn scales and arpeggios thoroughly. Unlike other woodwind instrumentalists, clarinettists must learn to negotiate that complex range of notes known as the 'break', an area in the middle of the treble stave which is particularly resistant to fluent playing in the early stages. Special care has to be taken here in order to achieve the desired effect.

This manual seeks to assist this situation by including a fingering chart, constant reminders in the form of simple symbols attached to each scale and arpeggio and useful advice appended to the examples most likely to be problematic. The aim is to help students learn their scales and arpeggios thoroughly, as well as provide support material for those woodwind teachers who may not be clarinet specialists.

It should be noted that the information given in this manual cannot apply in its entirety to the clarinet in C, which is catered for in Grades 1-5. Players of this instrument should adapt their fingering accordingly.

I am most grateful to Colin Honour, principal clarinettist with the English Northern Philharmonia (the orchestra of Opera North), who read the final draft of this manual and made many helpful suggestions.

IAN DENLEY   1995

DO NOT
PHOTOCOPY
© MUSIC

**The Associated Board of
the Royal Schools of Music**

Fingering chart

This comprehensive fingering chart and the notes given in the Guide to fingering on page 4 apply to the standard Boehm-system clarinet which has E as its lowest note. It lists the basic fingerings, as well as a choice of the more common alternatives. It does not pretend to be exhaustive.

First chart — notes: E, F, F#, G, G#, A, Bb, B, C, C#, D, Eb, E, F, F#, G, G#, A, Bb

	E	F	F#		G	G#	A	Bb	B	C	C#	D	Eb		E	F	F#		G	G#	A	Bb
Ref.	L	R	R	L	R	L		R			I	II			I	II			i	II		
LEFT HAND Thumb	Th	Th	Th	Th	Th	Th	Th	Th	Th	Th	Th	Th	Th	Th	Th	Th	Th	Th				Sp
1	●	●	●	●	●	●	●	●	●	●	●	●	●	●	○	●	○	○	○	G# ○	A ○	A ○
2	●	●	●	●	●	●	●	●	●	●	●	●	●	●	○	○	○	○	○	○	○	○
3	●	●	●	●	●	●	●	●	●	●	●	●	5a ○	○	○	○	○	○	○	○	○	○
4	1			2a		3a					C#	○	○	○	○	○	○	○	○	○	○	○
RIGHT HAND 1	●	●	●	●	●	●	●	●	○	●	○	○	5 ○	○	○	○	○	5+6 ○	○	○	○	○
2	●	●	●	●	●	●	●	○	●	○	○	○	○	○	○	○	○	○	○	○	○	○
3	●	●	●	●	●	●	●	○	7 ○	○	○	○	○	○	○	○	○	○	○	○	○	○
4	[2]	1a	2		3		4	○	○	○	○	○	○	○	○	○	○	○	○	○	○	○

Second chart — notes: B, C, C#, D, Eb, E, F, F#, G, G#, A, Bb, B, C

	B	C	C#		D	Eb	E	F	F#		G	G#	A	Bb		III*	IV		B	C
Ref.	L	R	R	L	R	L		R			I	II			I	II				
LEFT HAND Thumb	Sp Th	Sp Th	Sp Th	Sp Th	Sp Th	Sp Th	Sp Th	Sp Th	Sp Th	Sp Th	Sp Th	Sp Th	Sp Th	Sp Th	Sp Th	Sp Th	Sp Th	Sp Th	Sp Th	Sp Th
1	●	●	●	●	●	●	●	●	●	●	●	●	●	●	●	●	●	○		
2	●	●	●	●	●	●	●	●	●	●	●	●	●	○	○	○				
3													5a							
4	● 1	●	●	● 2a	●	● 3a	●	●	●	●	●	● C#	○	○	○	○	○			
RIGHT HAND 1	●	●	●	●	●	●	●	○	●	○	○	○	5 ○	○	●	○	○	○		
2	●	●	●	●	●	●	○	●	○	○	○	○	○	○	○	●	○	○		
3								7							(7)					
4	● [2]	● 1a	● 2	● 3	●	● 4	○	○	○	○	○	○	○	○	○	○	○			

Third chart — notes: C#, D, Eb, E, F, F#, G

	C#		D		Eb		E		F		F#				G				
Ref.	I	II	I	II	I	II	I	II	I*	II	II	III	IV	I	II	III	IV	V	
LEFT HAND Thumb	Sp Th	Sp Th	Sp Th	Sp Th	Sp Th	Sp Th	Sp Th	Sp Th	Sp Th	Sp Th	Sp Th	Sp Th	Sp Th	Sp Th	Sp Th	Sp Th	Sp Th	Sp Th	
1							G# ○								●	●	●	●	
2	○	○	○	○	○	○	●	●	●	●	●	●	○	●	○	○	○	○	
3	●	○	●	○	●	●	●	●	●	●	○	●	○	●	○	○	●	●	
4									C#	C#		C#	C#						
RIGHT HAND 1	●	5+6 ○	●	○	○	○	○	○	●	○	5 ●	○	●	●	●	○	●	●	
2	●	○	○	○	○	○	●	●	○	○	○	●	●	●	●	○	●	○	
3				7					(7)				7						
4	○	○	○ 4	● 4	● 4	○ 4	○ 4	○ (4)	○ 4	○ 4	○ 4	● 4	○ 4	○ 4	● 4	○ 4	● 4		

* Adding key 7 to this fingering helps the intonation.

 © 1995 by The Associated Board of the Royal Schools of Music

The following illustrations label the clarinet's key-work
and show how it will be referred to in this manual.

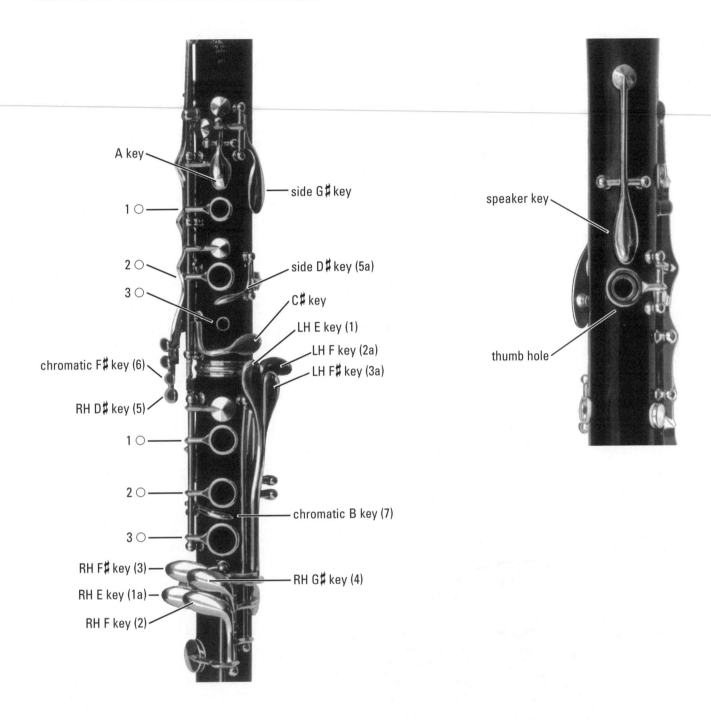

Key to symbols

LH	left hand	RH	right hand
●	cover hole	O	leave hole open
Th	cover thumb hole	Sp	press speaker key
1	press LH E key	1a	press RH E key
2	press RH F key	2a	press LH F key
3	press RH F♯ key	3a	press LH F♯ key
4	press RH G♯ key	C♯	press C♯ key
5	press RH D♯ key	5a	press side D♯ key
6	press chromatic F♯ key	7	press chromatic B key
A	press A key	G♯	press side G♯ key

NB: the fingering chart uses Thumb-1-2-3-4, unlike keyboard fingering (1-2-3-4-5)

Guide to fingering

For reference purposes, where notes are indicated throughout the manual with a small superscript number (e.g. Bb^1, E^2, $G\sharp^3$, etc.), this refers to their position within the clarinet's range:

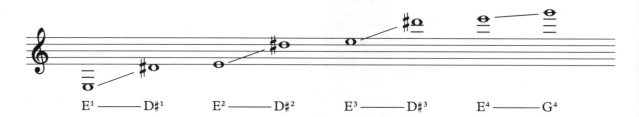

E^1 ——— $D\sharp^1$ E^2 ——— $D\sharp^2$ E^3 ——— $D\sharp^3$ E^4 ——— G^4

The 'Break'

Clarinettists will encounter the 'Break' in scales and arpeggios for the first time at Grade 2. There are three requirements for successful fingering across the Break: (i) as they lift, *all* fingers must remain very close to the keys and rings, most notably RH/1, which must not be allowed to stand upright against the edge of the RH D♯ key (key 5); (ii) if the note before the Break is A or B♭ (known as *throat* notes), the A and speaker keys must be merely touched with the side of LH/1 and the tip of the LH thumb respectively, not with the fleshy part; and (iii) the clarinet must be in perfect mechanical order, a fact frequently overlooked.

It should be noted that the RH fingers may be pressed down when playing any of the throat notes from G^2 to Bb^2. Besides assisting with break-crossing, this action greatly improves the quality of the throat notes.

Alternative fingerings

The clarinet has a set of basic fingerings, but there is a range of alternatives for certain situations, most notably duplicate keys for left-hand and right-hand 4th fingers. The following points should be noted.

Left-/right-hand 4th fingers   Although sliding fingers between keys is unavoidable in some clarinet repertoire, it is essentially an imperfect manœuvre, which is why instruments feature alternative 4th finger keys. No scale or arpeggio requires the clarinettist to slide the 4th finger of either hand and it is vital to basic technique that the correct alternative is used. In this manual, essential left-hand and right-hand 4th fingers are noted with 'L' or 'R' above the relevant note (see for example No.7). Where the use of a particular 4th finger is recommended, but not compulsory, 'L' or 'R' is given in brackets.

Other alternatives   Clarinet teachers are fairly evenly divided between insisting on one basic fingering or allowing alternatives. This manual does not insist on either, as this is a matter for the teacher. Where it is accepted that an alternative may be useful in promoting, for example, a smoother *legato*, the recommended fingering is indicated above the note with a roman numeral, referring to an alternative in the fingering chart (see for example No.3). Where further alternatives are available, they are indicated in brackets above the relevant note.

The top register   Clarinets vary greatly in their response and intonation above top C♯ ($C\sharp^3$), and a choice of fingering often has to be made. A set of alternatives is given in the fingering chart which focuses on ease of fingering at the top of the range, but secure intonation must be the guide, and therefore some experimentation is usually necessary.

Enharmonic note-names

Two or three notes having the same sound but different names are called *enharmonics*; for example, E♭ is the enharmonic of D♯. A full table is given below to guide students in the fingering of those notes in certain scales and arpeggios which may be unfamiliarly notated.

C	=	B♯	=	D♭♭		E	=	F♭	=	D×		G♯	=	A♭	
C♯	=	D♭	=	B×		F	=	E♯	=	G♭♭		A	=	G×	=	B♭♭
D	=	C×	=	E♭♭		F♯	=	G♭	=	E×		B♭	=	A♯	=	C♭♭
E♭	=	D♯	=	F♭♭		G	=	F×	=	A♭♭		B	=	C♭	=	A×

Notes on the requirements

Reference must always be made to the syllabus for the year in which the examination is to be taken, in case any changes have been made to the requirements.

In the examination, all scales and arpeggios must be played from memory.

Candidates should aim to play their scales and arpeggios at a pace that allows accuracy, with a uniform tone across all registers and a rhythmic flow without undue accentuation, as well as with even tonguing and good intonation. Recommended speeds are given on page 6.

In Grades 1-5 candidates may choose *either* the melodic *or* the harmonic form of the minor scale; in Grades 6-8 candidates are required to play *both* forms.

The choice of breathing place is left to the candidate's discretion, but taking a breath must not be allowed to disturb the flow of the scale or arpeggio. If a breath is taken during the course of a slurred scale or arpeggio, a *soft* tongue attack should be made on the note following the breath.

It is essential that students do not use a breath as a means of negotiating the break or octave.

Articulation

It is very important for the foundation of good articulation that players use the *tongue* to articulate, rather than just the breath, which is a common error at the elementary level. The sound must be well-supported from the diaphragm throughout all forms of articulation, so that the tone does not lose substance (usually with attendant intonation problems) or become brittle, especially when tonguing *staccato*.

Four different forms of articulation are found in the scale and arpeggio requirements: slurred, tongued, *legato*-tongued and *staccato*. In Grades 1-6 candidates are required to play scales and arpeggios both slurred and tongued; in Grades 7 and 8 candidates are required to play scales and arpeggios slurred, *legato*-tongued and *staccato*.

In slurred scales and arpeggios there is no gap between the notes, whereas the gap is large when playing *staccato*. In *legato*-tonguing the effect is almost slurred, but there is the smallest separation achieved by a very soft tongue attack. Scales and arpeggios involving a key signature with three or more sharps or flats will require special care with note-to-note finger co-ordination on the clarinet, especially when slurred.

The articulations may be visualized like this:

slurred   _____

tongued   ____   ____   ____   ____

legato-tongued   _____   _____   _____   _____

staccato   _   _   _   _

Legato-tonguing, perhaps the least familiar of the articulation forms required, may usefully be notated as follows:

Current requirements for Grades 1-8

This table lists scales and arpeggios required for each grade; numbers refer to those printed alongside the scales and arpeggios in the following pages.

Grade 1 9, 14, 51 *or* 52, 77, 82, 105

Grade 2 1, 10, 15, 27 *or* 28, 53 *or* 54, 69, 78, 83, 93, 106

Grade 3 2, 4, 10, 18, 20, 29 *or* 30, 45 *or* 46, 53 *or* 54, 59, 70, 72, 78, 86, 88, 94, 102, 106

Grade 4 5, 10, 15, 19, 21, 23 *or* 24, 29 *or* 30, 33 *or* 34, 45 *or* 46, 57 *or* 58, 60, 62, 73, 78, 83, 87, 89, 91, 94, 96, 102, 108, 109

Grade 5 2, 5, 6, 7, 15, 17, 21, 23 *or* 24, 25 *or* 26, 29 *or* 30, 37 *or* 38, 41 *or* 42, 57 *or* 58, 60, 62, 70, 73, 74, 75, 83, 85, 89, 91, 92, 94, 98, 100, 108, 109, 112, 120, 132

Grade 6 3, 5, 6, 8, 17, 21, 22, 25, 26, 35, 36, 49, 50, 53, 54, 55, 56, 57, 58, 60, 61, 62, 63, 71, 73, 74, 76, 85, 89, 90, 92, 97, 104, 106, 107, 108, 112, 119, 120, 124, 129

Grade 7 2, 3, 5, 6, 8, 11, 12, 15, 17, 19, 21, 22, 23, 24, 25, 26, 29, 30, 31, 32, 35, 36, 39, 40, 41, 42, 45, 46, 49, 50, 53, 54, 55, 56, 57, 58, (Chromatic scale requirements: see note to No.64), 70, 71, 73, 74, 76, 79, 80, 83, 85, 87, 89, 90, 91, 92, 94, 95, 97, 99, 100, 102, 104, 106, 107, 108, 111, 113, 116, 117, 119, 121, 124, 129, 130

Grade 8 ALL NUMBERS MUST BE LEARNED, with the following exceptions:
1, 4, 7, 9, 10, 12, 14, 15, 18, 20, 27, 28, 33, 34, 37, 38, 41, 42, 45, 46, 51, 52, 69, 72, 75, 77, 78, 80, 82, 83, 86, 88, 93, 96, 98, 100, 102, 105, 109, 120, 122, 128, 132

(Chromatic scale requirements: see note to No.64)

Recommended speeds

The following recommended *minimum* speeds are given as a general guide. It is essential that scales and arpeggios are played at a speed steady enough to allow a well-focused sound with good intonation across the range, yet rapid enough to allow well-organized breathing without impairing fingering and tonal clarity.

major and minor scales, chromatic scales, scales in thirds, whole-tone scales, dominant and diminished sevenths			*major and minor arpeggios*		
Grade 1	♩ =	50	♪ =	72
Grade 2	♩ =	56	♪ =	80
Grade 3	♩ =	66	♪ =	92
Grade 4	♩ =	72	♪ =	100
Grade 5	♩ =	80	♪ =	112
Grade 6	♩ =	104	♩. =	56
Grade 7	♩ =	116	♩. =	66
Grade 8	♩ =	132	♩. =	76

Major Scales

1 C MAJOR 1 Octave

1: the first scale which involves crossing the Break. Keep your fingers really close to the keys and rings as you ascend.

2 C MAJOR 2 Octaves

3 D♭ MAJOR 2 Octaves

3: it is possible to use fingering II for D♭^{3}, but care must be taken with tuning.

4 D MAJOR 1 Octave

4 and 5: if using key 1 [LH/4] for B above the Break, *do not* put down key 2 [RH/4] at the same time; keep RH/4 free for key 3.

5 D MAJOR 2 Octaves

Grade

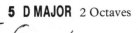

6 E♭ MAJOR 2 Octaves

7 E MAJOR 2 Octaves

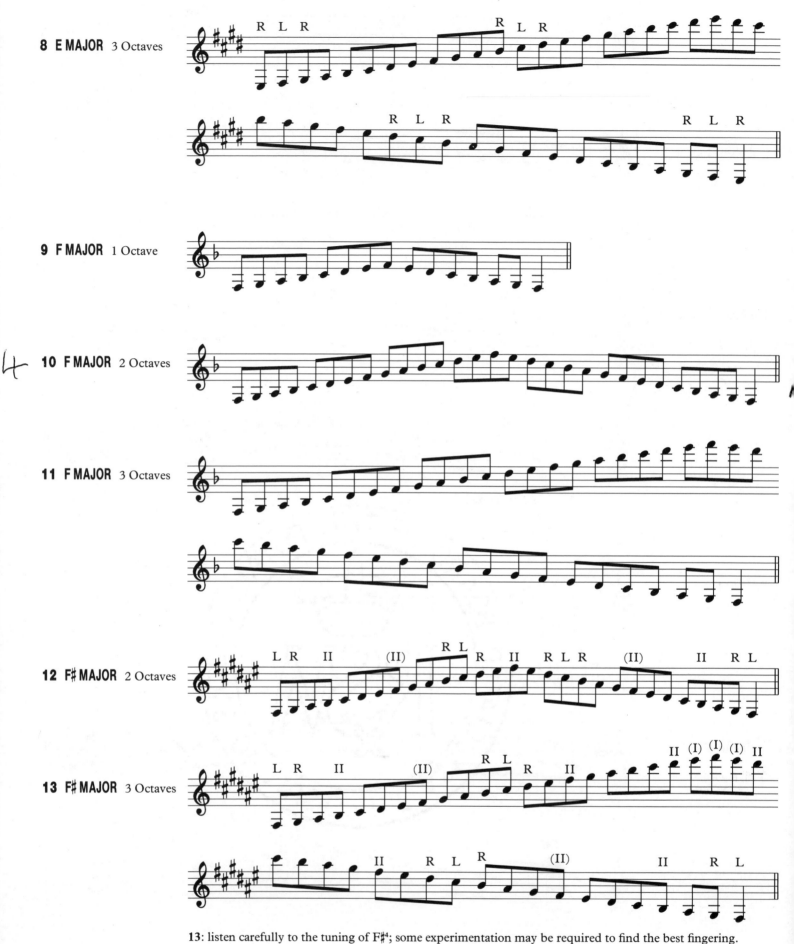

8 E MAJOR 3 Octaves

9 F MAJOR 1 Octave

10 F MAJOR 2 Octaves

11 F MAJOR 3 Octaves

12 F♯ MAJOR 2 Octaves

13 F♯ MAJOR 3 Octaves

13: listen carefully to the tuning of F♯⁴; some experimentation may be required to find the best fingering.

14 G MAJOR 1 Octave

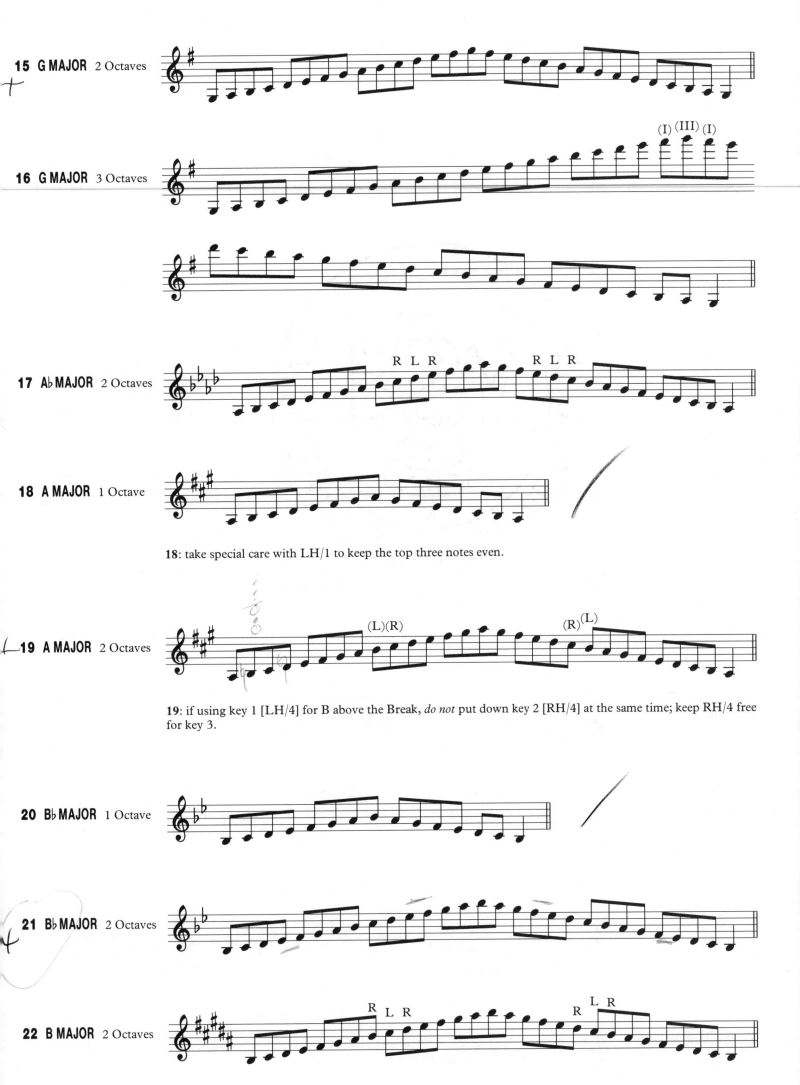

18: take special care with LH/1 to keep the top three notes even.

19: if using key 1 [LH/4] for B above the Break, *do not* put down key 2 [RH/4] at the same time; keep RH/4 free for key 3.

Minor Scales

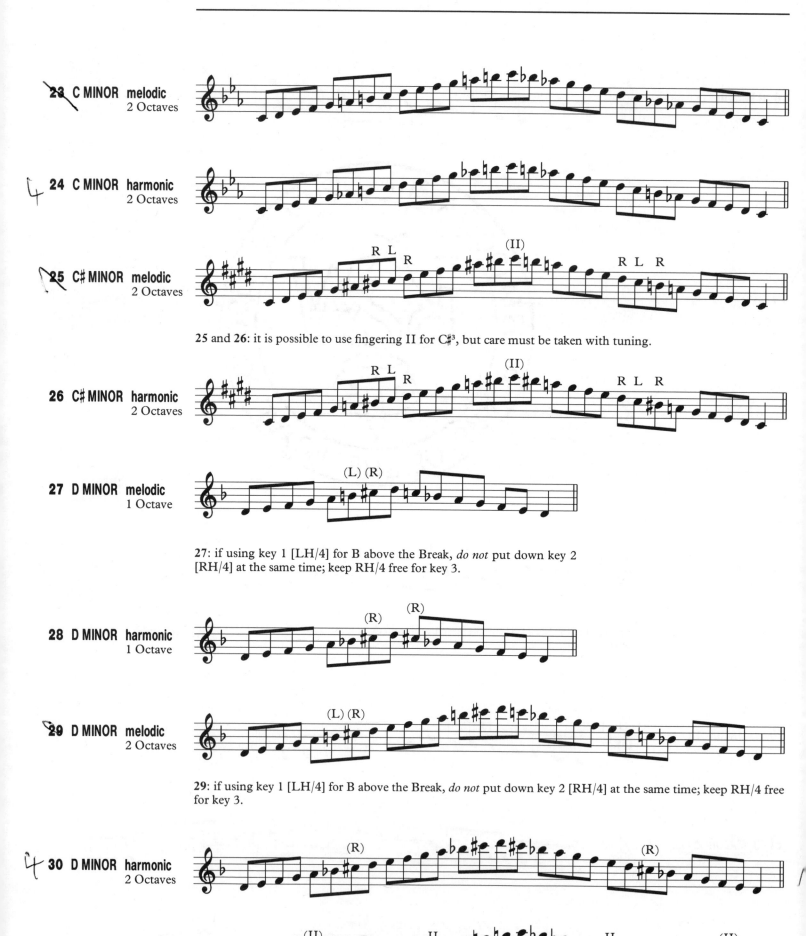

23 C MINOR melodic
2 Octaves

24 C MINOR harmonic
2 Octaves

25 C# MINOR melodic
2 Octaves

25 and 26: it is possible to use fingering II for C#³, but care must be taken with tuning.

26 C# MINOR harmonic
2 Octaves

27 D MINOR melodic
1 Octave

27: if using key 1 [LH/4] for B above the Break, *do not* put down key 2 [RH/4] at the same time; keep RH/4 free for key 3.

28 D MINOR harmonic
1 Octave

29 D MINOR melodic
2 Octaves

29: if using key 1 [LH/4] for B above the Break, *do not* put down key 2 [RH/4] at the same time; keep RH/4 free for key 3.

30 D MINOR harmonic
2 Octaves

31 Eb MINOR melodic
2 Octaves

AB 2447

32 E♭ MINOR harmonic
2 Octaves

33 E MINOR melodic
2 Octaves

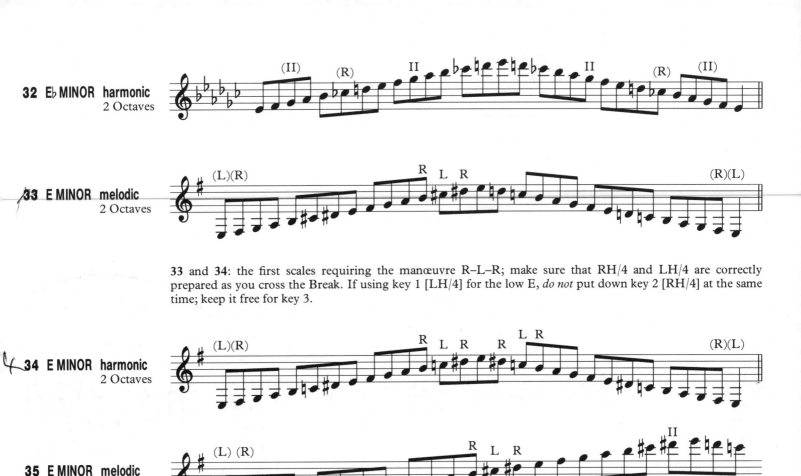

33 and **34**: the first scales requiring the manœuvre R–L–R; make sure that RH/4 and LH/4 are correctly prepared as you cross the Break. If using key 1 [LH/4] for the low E, *do not* put down key 2 [RH/4] at the same time; keep it free for key 3.

34 E MINOR harmonic
2 Octaves

35 E MINOR melodic
3 Octaves

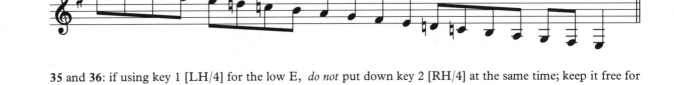

35 and **36**: if using key 1 [LH/4] for the low E, *do not* put down key 2 [RH/4] at the same time; keep it free for key 3.

36 E MINOR harmonic
3 Octaves

37 F MINOR melodic
2 Octaves

38 F MINOR harmonic
2 Octaves

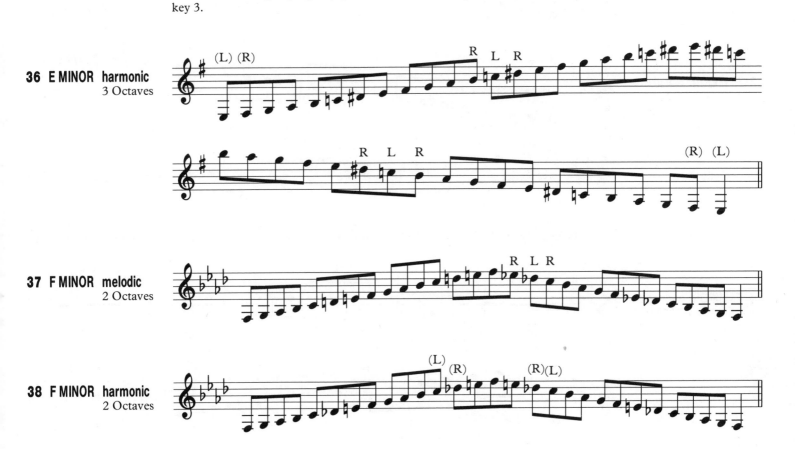

39 F MINOR melodic
3 Octaves

40 F MINOR harmonic
3 Octaves

41 F♯ MINOR melodic
2 Octaves

41: for high F♯, it is best not to use fingering II, as the note is followed by E♮ and not E♯.

42 F♯ MINOR harmonic
2 Octaves

43 F♯ MINOR melodic
3 Octaves

43 and 44: listen carefully to the tuning of F♯⁴; some experimentation may be required to find the best fingering.

44 F♯ MINOR harmonic
3 Octaves

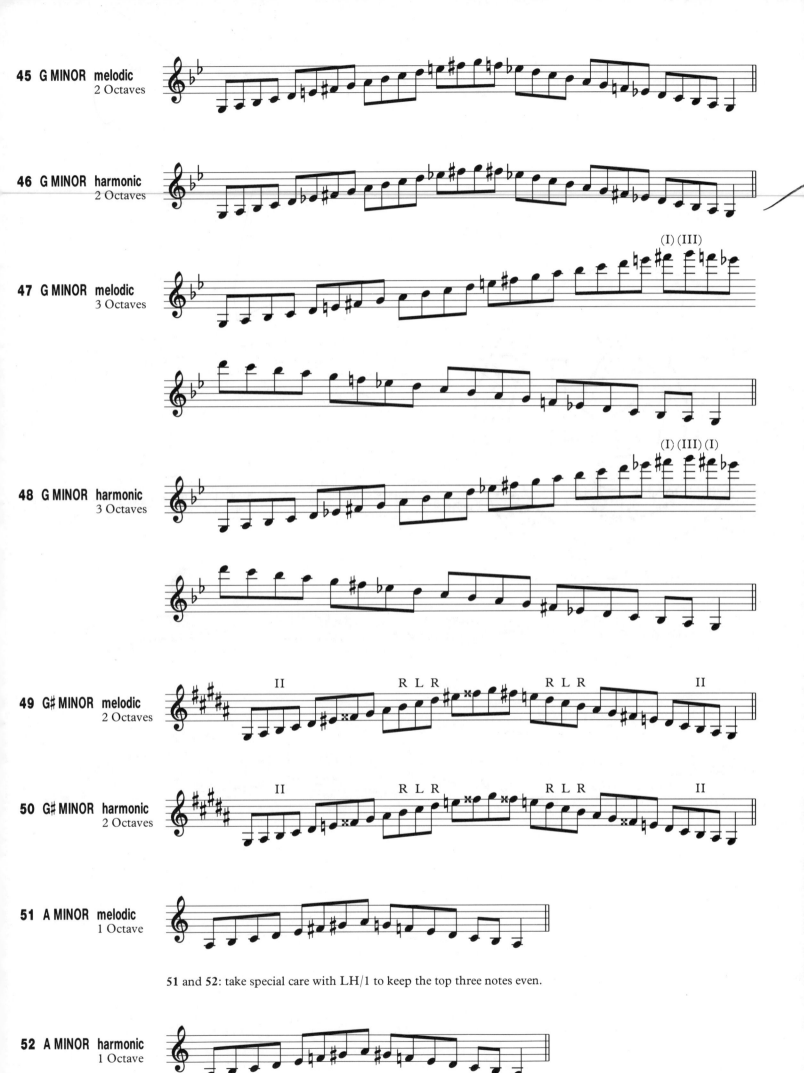

45 G MINOR melodic
2 Octaves

46 G MINOR harmonic
2 Octaves

47 G MINOR melodic
3 Octaves

48 G MINOR harmonic
3 Octaves

49 G# MINOR melodic
2 Octaves

50 G# MINOR harmonic
2 Octaves

51 A MINOR melodic
1 Octave

51 and **52**: take special care with LH/1 to keep the top three notes even.

52 A MINOR harmonic
1 Octave

53 A MINOR melodic
2 Octaves

54 A MINOR harmonic
2 Octaves

55 Bb MINOR melodic
2 Octaves

56 Bb MINOR harmonic
2 Octaves

57 B MINOR melodic
2 Octaves

58 B MINOR harmonic
2 Octaves

Chromatic Scales

59 on C 1 Octave

60 on C 2 Octaves

Grade K.

61 on E 3 Octaves

62 on F 2 Octaves

GRADE 4.

63 on A 2 Octaves

64 from low E to top G

The chromatic scale requirements for Grades 7 and 8 can be taken from No.64 above.

Grade 7   On E and F – 3 octaves
On any other note – 2 octaves

Grade 8   On any note from E to G – 3 octaves
On any other note – 2 octaves

Scales in Thirds

65 C MAJOR 2 Octaves

65 and **66**: take special care when negotiating the Break.

66 D MAJOR 2 Octaves

Whole-Tone Scales

67 on B 2 Octaves

68 on C 2 Octaves

Major Arpeggios

NOTE: In most arpeggios, if the note after the Break involves a 4th finger, using RH/4 is recommended where possible, as this helps the arpeggio's evenness and stability. Exceptions are clearly indicated with an 'L'.

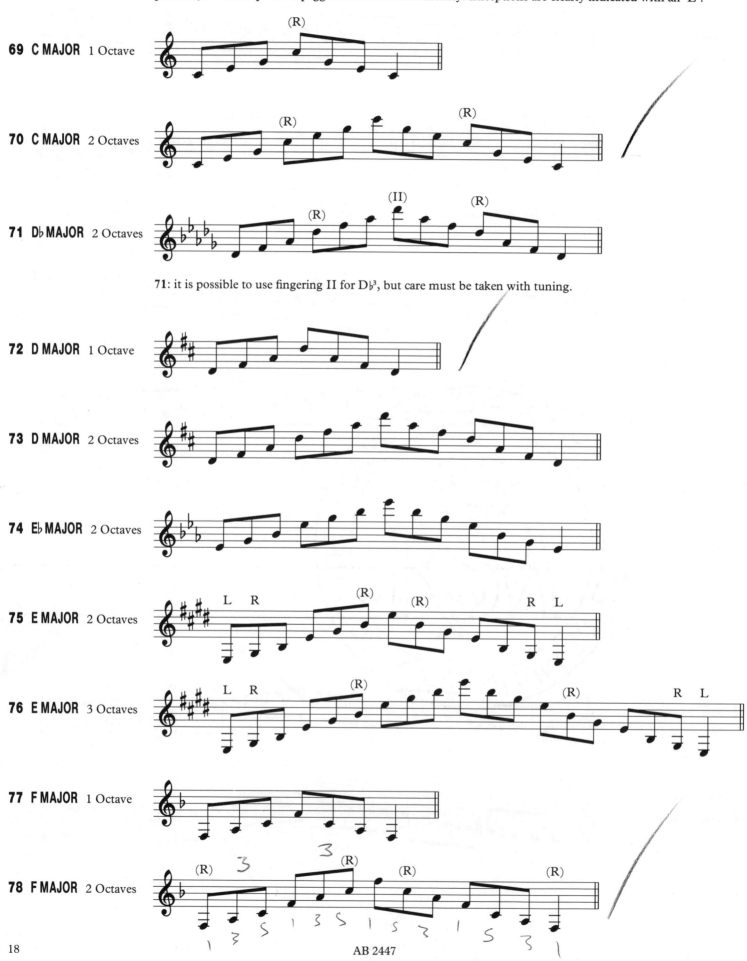

69 **C MAJOR** 1 Octave

70 **C MAJOR** 2 Octaves

71 **Db MAJOR** 2 Octaves

71: it is possible to use fingering II for Db³, but care must be taken with tuning.

72 **D MAJOR** 1 Octave

73 **D MAJOR** 2 Octaves

74 **Eb MAJOR** 2 Octaves

75 **E MAJOR** 2 Octaves

76 **E MAJOR** 3 Octaves

77 **F MAJOR** 1 Octave

78 **F MAJOR** 2 Octaves

AB 2447

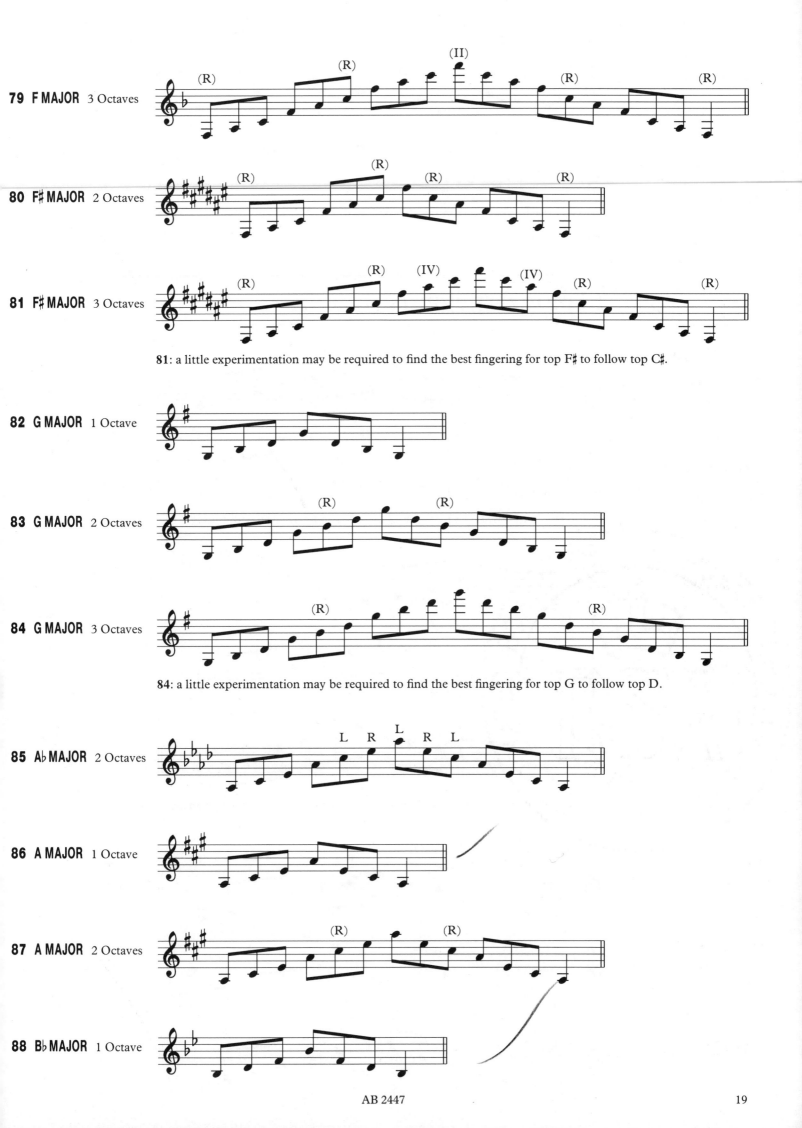

79 F MAJOR 3 Octaves

80 F♯ MAJOR 2 Octaves

81 F♯ MAJOR 3 Octaves

81: a little experimentation may be required to find the best fingering for top F♯ to follow top C♯.

82 G MAJOR 1 Octave

83 G MAJOR 2 Octaves

84 G MAJOR 3 Octaves

84: a little experimentation may be required to find the best fingering for top G to follow top D.

85 A♭ MAJOR 2 Octaves

86 A MAJOR 1 Octave

87 A MAJOR 2 Octaves

88 B♭ MAJOR 1 Octave

89 **B♭ MAJOR** 2 Octaves

90 **B MAJOR** 2 Octaves

90: RH/1 needs special care in negotiating low B–D♯ really cleanly, especially when slurred.

Minor Arpeggios

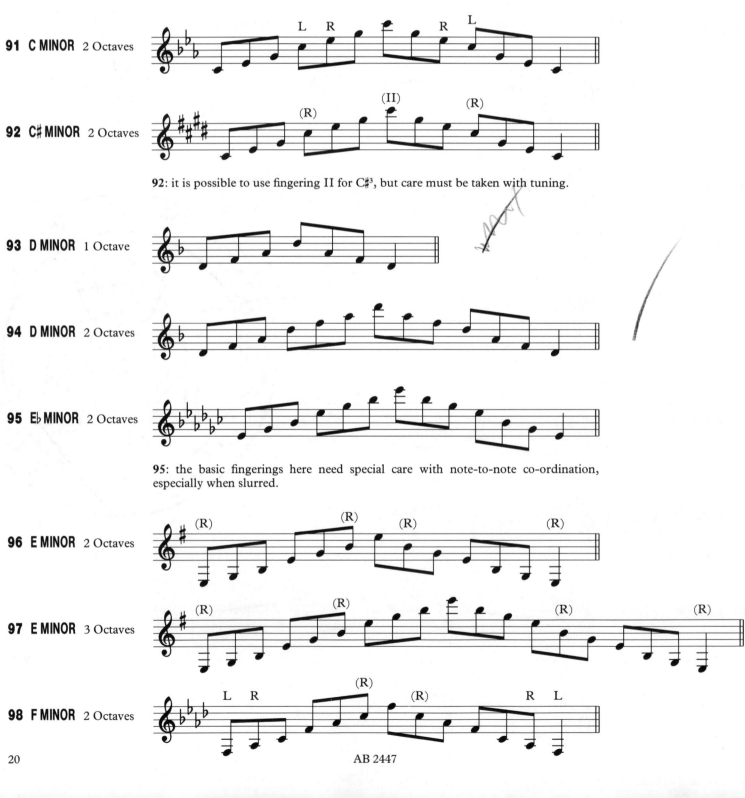

91 **C MINOR** 2 Octaves

92 **C♯ MINOR** 2 Octaves

92: it is possible to use fingering II for C♯³, but care must be taken with tuning.

93 **D MINOR** 1 Octave

94 **D MINOR** 2 Octaves

95 **E♭ MINOR** 2 Octaves

95: the basic fingerings here need special care with note-to-note co-ordination, especially when slurred.

96 **E MINOR** 2 Octaves

97 **E MINOR** 3 Octaves

98 **F MINOR** 2 Octaves

AB 2447

99 F MINOR 3 Octaves

100 F♯ MINOR 2 Octaves

101 F♯ MINOR 3 Octaves

101: a little experimentation may be required to find the best fingering for top F♯ to follow top C♯.

102 G MINOR 2 Octaves

103 G MINOR 3 Octaves

103: a little experimentation may be required to find the best fingering for top G to follow top D.

104 G♯ MINOR 2 Octaves

104: RH/1 needs special care in negotiating low B–D♯ really cleanly, especially when slurred.

105 A MINOR 1 Octave

106 A MINOR 2 Octaves

107 B♭ MINOR 2 Octaves

108 B MINOR 2 Octaves

Dominant Sevenths

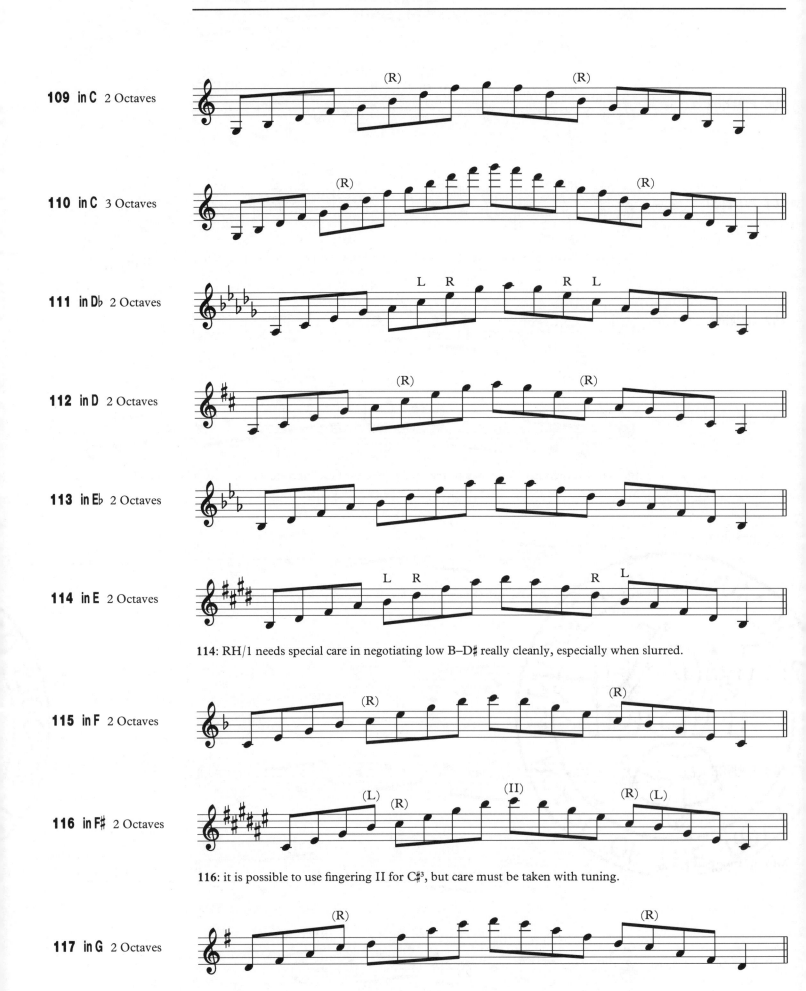

109 in C 2 Octaves

110 in C 3 Octaves

111 in Db 2 Octaves

112 in D 2 Octaves

113 in Eb 2 Octaves

114 in E 2 Octaves

114: RH/1 needs special care in negotiating low B–D# really cleanly, especially when slurred.

115 in F 2 Octaves

116 in F# 2 Octaves

116: it is possible to use fingering II for C#³, but care must be taken with tuning.

117 in G 2 Octaves

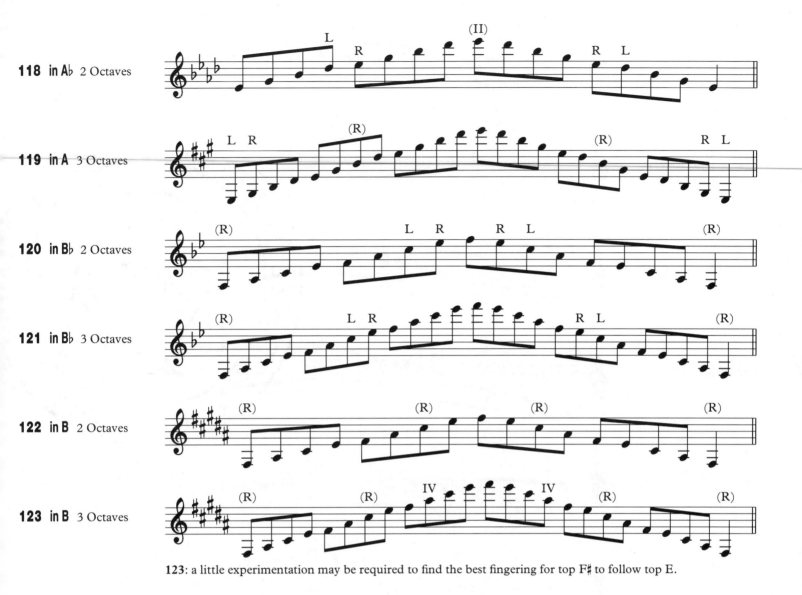

123: a little experimentation may be required to find the best fingering for top F♯ to follow top E.

Diminished Sevenths

AB 2447

Music and text origination by
Barnes Music Engraving Ltd, East Sussex
Printed by Caligraving Ltd, Thetford, Norfolk

5:05